CONTENTS

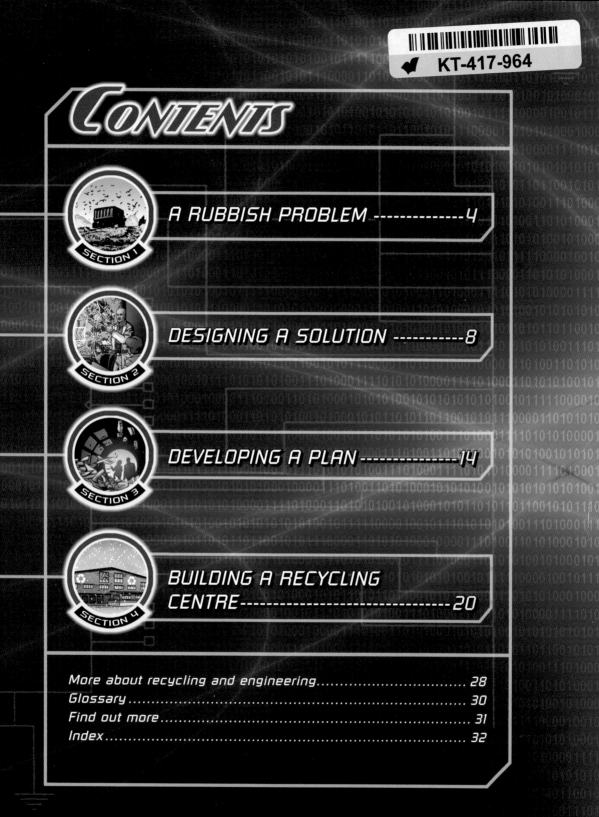

A text message sends Max Axiom, Super Scientist, on an engineering adventure.

It's an urgent message from Mayor Richardson.

BZZZT!
BZZZT!
BZZZT!

Help! The city's landfill site is filling up quickly.

GRAPHIC SCIENCE AND ENGINEERING IN ACTION

ENGINEERING AN AWESOME
RECYCLING CENTRE
WITH MAX AXIOM
SUPER SCIENTIST

by Nikole Brooks Bethea

illustrated by Pop Art Studios

Raintree

Raintree is an imprint of Capstone Global Library Limited, a company incorporated in England and Wales having its registered office at 7 Pilgrim Street, London, EC4V 6LB – Registered company number: 6695582

To contact Raintree please phone 0845 6044371, fax + 44 (0) 1865 312263, or email myorders@ raintreepublishers.co.uk. Customers from outside the UK please telephone +44 1865 312262.

First published by Capstone Press in 2013
First published in the United Kingdom in 2014
The moral rights of the proprietor have been asserted.

Designer
Ted Williams

Cover Illustrator
Marcelo Baez

Media Researcher
Wanda Winch

Production Specialist
Laura Manthe

Editor
Christopher L. Harbo

Originated by Capstone Global Library Ltd
Printed and bound in China by LEO Paper Products Ltd

ISBN 978 1 406 26685 6
17 16 15 14 13
10 9 8 7 6 5 4 3 2 1

A full catalogue record for this book is available from the British Library.

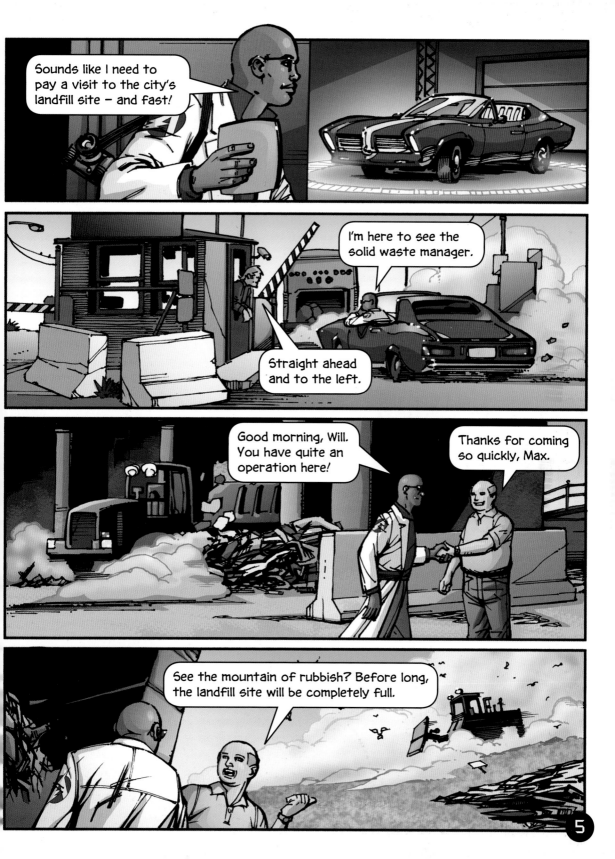

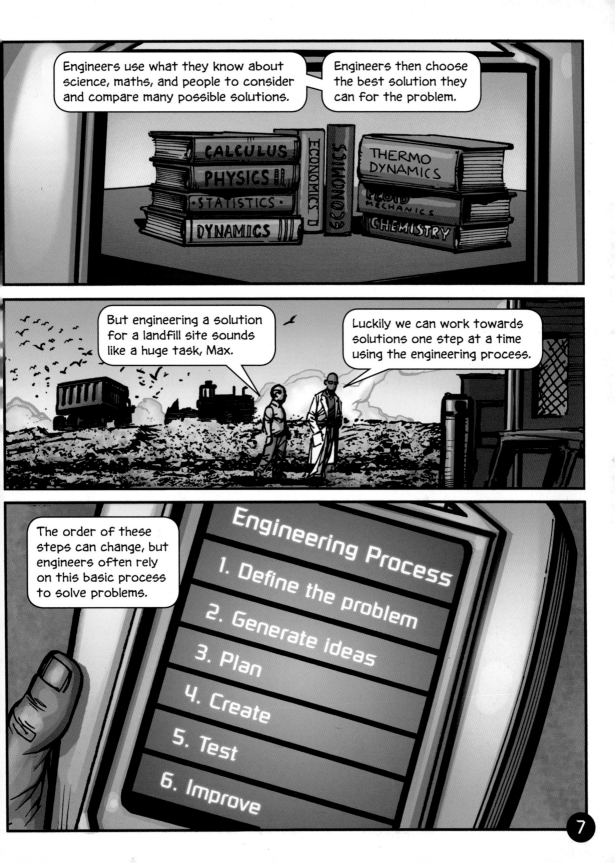

DEPARTMENT OF
ENVIRONMENTAL PROTECTION
Solid waste laws, regulations,
and policies

Chapter 32, Section 4

I've researched solid waste laws and treatment processes. I've also interviewed solid waste managers in other counties to see how they handled similar problems.

Our problem is that the landfill site is running out of space. To solve it, we'll start the second step of the engineering process – generating ideas.

One idea is for the city to buy a large piece of land to build a new landfill site.

Building an incinerator is a second idea. An incinerator would burn most of the waste. Little waste would go to the landfill site.

Of course, much of the plastic, metal, glass, paper, and cardboard sent to the landfill site could be recycled.

Building a recycling centre is a third idea.

GAR-BARGE

In 1987 the *Mobro 4000* barge left New York, USA carrying more than 2800 tonnes of rubbish. It travelled 9,660 kilometres (6,000 miles) looking for a place to dispose of the rubbish. It was nicknamed the Gar-barge. Six US states and three countries turned the barge away. After six months, it returned to New York. The rubbish was burned in an incinerator. Afterwards recycling increased because people became aware of waste disposal issues.

Thanks for meeting me at such short notice, Will and Mayor Richardson. I put together a few ideas for solving our landfill problem.

I found empty land in this part of the city. My first idea is to build a new landfill site here.

But when I visited the site, I discovered that the city's drinking water wells are nearby. Environmental laws will not allow a landfill site this close to the wells.

I guess we can rule out building a new landfill site there.

My next idea is to build an incinerator to burn the solid waste. But I'm concerned an incinerator could lower the value of nearby homes. Incinerators could also release pollution into the air.

The city council doesn't want to upset citizens. Do you have any other possible solutions?

Many communities have solved this problem by sorting out the materials that can be recycled. My third idea is to build a recycling centre.

A recycling centre is basically a large rubbish sorter. Machines separate out each of the recyclable materials. Manufacturers buy these sorted recyclables to make new products.

I think we have the solution to the city's waste problem.

Welcome, Max. I'm Gloria Garcia, the recycling centre manager.

Nice to meet you. Tell me how your recycling centre works.

Screening is the first step in our process. This drum-shaped trommel screen spins. Materials tumble around inside it. Glass bottles, plastic bottles, and cans fall through the holes in the screen.

That leaves only cardboard and paper inside the screen.

The cardboard and paper are baled and sent to a manufacturer to be made into new products.

Here, a magnet pulls iron and steel materials from the conveyor belt.

Aluminium is a metal. But it's not magnetic. How are the drinks cans sorted?

We use an eddy current separator. It has fast, rotating magnets in it. They create a force to repel aluminium.

The cans leap off the conveyor belt!

Only glass and plastic containers need to be separated now.

Resin identification codes

Look at the bottom of a plastic container. The number inside a triangle of arrows is a resin identification code (RIC). The RIC stands for the type of plastic used to make the container. Number 1 stands for polyethylene terephthalate (PET), a plastic used in water bottles. Number 2 stands for high density polyethylene (HDPE), which is used in washing-up liquid bottles and milk cartons. Although the triangle looks like a recycling symbol, not all plastics with RICs can be recycled. Check with your local recycler to see which numbers are accepted.

This optical scanner sorts plastics. The scanner recognizes the type of plastic by the way it reflects light.

What a cool engineering solution.

I hear puffs of air.

Yes. The air blows the plastic into the correct collection container. The glass simply falls off the end of the conveyor.

GLASS

PLASTIC

This is a great design for our new recycling centre. Everything is sorted based on the materials' physical properties.

At a paper mill, paper and water are mixed and blended to make a slurry. The slurry is washed, screened, and made into new paper products by machines designed by engineers.

Metals are shredded at a metal smelter. Then they are melted and made into metal bars. These bars are made into new metal products.

At a glass reclaimer, glass is crushed and mixed with sand, a powder called soda ash, and limestone. Then, it is melted and shaped into new glass materials.

Finally, at the plastics reprocessing plant, plastics are washed and ground into flakes. The flakes are melted and formed into pellets. These pellets can be turned into new plastic products.

It's a message from Will. During testing he discovered that manufacturers need cardboard bundled separately from the other paper types.

Discovering your design could be better is disappointing. But it's really just part of the engineering process. Our next step is to improve the design.

BZZZT! BZZZT! BZZZT!

Hmm. So, how can we separate cardboard from other papers?

Why don't we add a sorting screen? We'll install it after the trommel screen. It will separate cardboard from the other papers.

The stiff cardboard rolls over the discs. The thinner paper will fall between the discs.

Thank you, Max. Cardboard and paper are now sorted separately.

MORE ABOUT
RECYCLING AND ENGINEERING

Between 2011 and 2012, the average British citizen created around 1.18 kilograms of rubbish each day. The total amount of waste handled by local authorities was 25.6 million tonnes. But not all of it went to landfill sites. Forty-two per cent, or 10.7 million tonnes, was recycled, composted, or reused.

Engineers and scientists have found ways to reuse recycled materials. Rubber from old tyres is ground and blended with asphalt to build roads. Glassphalt is the name given to asphalt that uses crushed glass. Glassphalt roads often shimmer when headlights shine on them.

Materials engineers have developed a building material from recycled plastic bottles and other waste plastics. This material was used to build a bridge in Scotland. The bridge is 27.4 metres (90 feet) long, 3.7 metres (12 feet) wide, and crosses the River Tweed. Recycling the plastic materials kept 45.4 tonnes of plastic from going into landfill. In addition, the new bridge won't rust or need paint.

Solid waste engineers have an important job when designing landfill sites. They stop solid waste in the site from polluting soil and water. Engineers build landfill sites away from sensitive places such as lakes, marshes, and areas that flood. Engineers design liners to keep harmful liquids from flowing out of the site. Pump and piping systems are designed to remove harmful liquids from the site. Engineers design monitoring wells that make sure that groundwater hasn't been polluted. Engineers also design drainage systems to allow stormwater to flow away from the landfill site.

Treatment of waste water, or sewage, is a modern engineering marvel. Engineers design large systems of underground pipes that carry waste water away from homes and businesses. It is sent to waste water treatment plants where it is cleaned. Engineers design different steps to clean the waste water. Larger solids are removed by screening. Settling tanks and skimmer devices remove materials that sink or float. Small organisms are used to eat the waste materials. Chemicals kill any remaining harmful materials before the water is released back into lakes, rivers, or groundwater.

MORE ABOUT

SUPER SCIENTIST

Real name: Maxwell J. Axiom
Home town: Seattle, USA
Height: 1.86 m   **Weight:** 87 kg
Eyes: Brown   **Hair:** None

Super capabilities: Super intelligence; able to shrink to the size of an atom; sunglasses give x-ray vision; lab coat allows for travel through time and space.

Origin: Since birth, Max Axiom seemed destined for greatness. His mother, a marine biologist, taught her son about the mysteries of the sea. His father, a nuclear physicist and volunteer park warden, schooled Max on the wonders of the earth and sky.

One day while Max was hiking in the hills, a mega-charged lightning bolt struck him with blinding fury. When he awoke, he discovered a new-found energy and set out to learn as much about science as possible. He travelled the globe studying every aspect of the subject. Then he was ready to share his knowledge and new identity with the world. He had become Max Axiom, Super Scientist.

Glossary

asphalt black tar that is mixed with sand and gravel to make roads

barge large, flat-bottomed boat used for transporting heavy goods, mainly on rivers and canals

blueprint diagram that shows how to construct a building or other project

compost make vegetable matter or manure into soil

density amount of mass an object or substance has based on its volume

eddy current separator machine that uses a strong, circular magnetic field to separate metals from non-metals

incinerator furnace for burning rubbish and other waste materials

landfill solid waste that is buried in the ground

optical scanner machine that uses a light beam to recognize text, images, or materials

organism living thing such as a plant, animal, bacterium, or fungus

recyclable thing that can be used again

resin sticky substance created and used to make plastics

slurry mixture of paper and water

smelter factory for melting metal

trommel screen rotating drum used to separate materials by size

FIND OUT MORE

Books

Earth-Friendly Crafts: Clever Ways to Reuse Everyday Items, Kathy Ross (Millbrook Press, 2009)

Recycling: Reducing Waste (Do It Yourself), Buffy Silverman (Raintree, 2008)

Waste Crisis (Planet in Crisis), Steve Parker and Russ Parker (Rosen Central, 2009)

Waste and Recycling (Can the Earth Cope?), Louise Spilsbury (Wayland, 2013)

Websites

www.clean-air-kids.org.uk/recycling1.html
Check out this website to find out how you can recycle your household waste.

www.ollierecycles.com/uk/index.html
Join Ollie and his friends and learn all about how you can reduce, reuse, and recycle.

www.runnymede.gov.uk/portal/site/recycling/
Kids_learn_recycling/
Visit this website to find out how what you can do to help with recycling.

INDEX